Tricky Logic Puzzles

Norman D. Willis
Illustrated by Jim Sharpe

Sterling Publishing Co., Inc.   New York

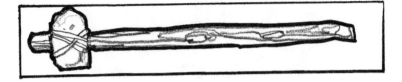

Edited by Claire Bazinet

Library of Congress Cataloging-in-Publication Data

Willis, Norman D.
    Tricky Logic Puzzles / by Norman D. Willis ; illustrated by
Jim Sharpe.
        p.   cm.
    Includes index.
    ISBN 0-8069-3805-6
    1. Puzzles. 2. Logic I. Sharpe, Jim. II. Title.
GV1493.W4966   1995
793.73—dc20   95-36264
                                                        CIP

10 9 8 7 6 5 4 3 2 1

Published by Sterling Publishing Company, Inc.
387 Park Avenue South, New York, N.Y. 10016
© 1995 by Norman D. Willis
Distributed in Canada by Sterling Publishing
c/o Canadian Manda Group, One Atlantic Avenue, Suite 105
Toronto, Ontario, Canada M6K 3E7
Distributed in Great Britain and Europe by Cassell PLC
Wellington House, 125 Strand, London WC2R 0BB, England
Distributed in Australia by Capricorn Link (Australia) Pty Ltd.
P.O. Box 6651, Baulkham Hills, Business Centre, NSW 2153, Australia
Manufactured in the United States of America

Sterling ISBN 0-8069-3805-6

To my wife, Judith,
whose ideas and quality review
contributed significantly to this book

Contents

Before You Begin   **6**

1. The Dragons of Lidd   **8**
    1-1 One Dragon* 9
    1-2 Another Dragon* 9
    1-3 Two Types* 9
    1-4 Two Colors* 10
    1-5 Three Dragons* 10
    1-6 Who Speaks the Truth?* 11
    1-7 Three and One** 11
    1-8 Four Dragons** 12

2. The Adventures of Captain Jean Lafoot, the Pirate   **13**
    2-1 One Overslept* 14
    2-2 A Chase on the Open Sea* 14
    2-3 Buccaneer Quartet* 15
    2-4 A Sea Serpent* 15
    2-5 The Island Fish* 16
    2-6 The Musket Competition** 17
    2-7 Whose Hair Turned White?** 18
    2-8 The Sea Serpent Returns*** 19

3. The Minikins   **20**
    3-1 Narrow Escapes* 21
    3-2 Homes of the Minikins* 21
    3-3 Musicians* 23
    3-4 A Skirmish* 24
    3-5 Potluck Dinner** 25
    3-6 Athletic Competition** 25
    3-7 River Trip** 26
    3-8 Autumn Festival and Games** 27

4. Hyperborea   28

4-1 Apollo Meets Two* 29
4-2 Apollo Meets Two More* 29
4-3 Delegation from Æthiopia* 30
4-4 Who Speaks Truthfully?* 31
4-5 Who Won the Olive Wreath?* 32
4-6 The Centaur Prophet* 32
4-7 A Chimaera in the Land** 34
4-8 Who Is the Outlier?*** 35
4-9 Some Are More Equal Than Others*** 36

5. Nonsense   38

5-1 Rabbits Play Hockey* 39
5-2 Gorillas Enjoy Ballet* 39
5-3 No Books in the Second Solar Period of
     the Week* 40
5-4 Sentient Beings* 41
5-5 Neighbors Make Good Fences** 42

6. The Land of Liars   43

6-1 Two Inhabitants* 44
6-2 Two Inhabitants Again* 44
6-3 Two Inhabitants Once Again* 45
6-4 Three Inhabitants* 45
6-5 Three Inhabitants Again** 46
6-6 Morning and Afternoon** 46
6-7 Four Inhabitants*** 47

Hints   48
Solutions   59
Index   96

Before You Begin

Puzzle solving is an ancient form of entertainment. Such famous Greek scholars as Aristotle and Homer found puzzles to be a source of interest and challenge.

Today, we still look to puzzles for enjoyment. Logic puzzles, which involve the application of deductive reasoning to given propositions or statements, are an excellent means of expanding your mental power. The challenge lies in taking the information provided in each puzzle, forming conclusions, and arriving at the solution. This requires no prior knowledge, only your own natural ability to reason logically.

The logic puzzles in this book are of varying difficulty. Within each section they are generally arranged in ascending order—from the more easily solved to the more complicated. In a given section, you may want to start with the first puzzle and work your way to those that are more difficult. They are graded from one to three asterisks, as follows:

     * Challenging
   ** Tantalizing
 *** Mind Expanding

If you find that a particular puzzle or type of puzzle seems insurmountable, the Hints section, following the puzzles, will be helpful. Solutions, including supporting considerations where these are appropriate, follow the Hints section.

Here are three suggestions that will be helpful to you in solving logic puzzles:

1. For most puzzles, it is useful to construct diagrams to help in your search for solutions. Suggested examples can be found in both the Hints and Solutions sections. Use of a diagram will aid in analyzing tentative assumptions and in organizing conclusions as you review the data provided in each puzzle.

2. It is important that, if you are having difficulty with a puzzle, you resist turning to the solution until you are convinced you have given it your best effort.

3. Finally, if you do have to refer to the answer, carefully examine the approach that is explained in the considerations leading to the solution. You will be able to use the method to solve other puzzles of the same type—and you will find yourself successfully solving more difficult puzzles.

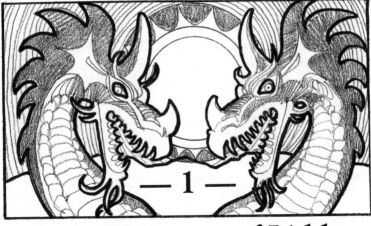

The Dragons of Lidd

There are two types of dragons in the Kingdom of Lidd. Rational dragons, being sensible, have determined that devouring farm animals and their owners is, in the long run, not healthy for dragons. Predator dragons, on the other hand, respond to their instincts and refuse to do otherwise, nor do they show any fear of humans.

Dragons in Lidd are also of two different colors related to their veracity. Red rational dragons always lie; and grey rational dragons always tell the truth. Red predator dragons always tell the truth; and grey predator dragons always lie.

Because dragons are few in number and are considered an endangered species, the King has decreed that rational dragons shall be protected, and that any knight caught slaying a rational dragon will be dealt with severely.

It would help to know which dragons are rationals and which are predators. It would also help to know a dragon's color. (If one catches a red dragon in a lie, one would know that he is a rational.) Unfortunately, there is an affliction endemic to humans in Lidd: they are color-blind. To them, all dragons look grey.

P1–1 One Dragon*

A knight in full armor and riding a horse approaches a dragon and asks his color and type. Grey rational dragons and red predator dragons always tell the truth; red rational dragons and grey predator dragons always lie.

Dragon: I am a grey predator.

What is he?

(Hint on page 48)
(Solution on page 59)

P1–2 Another Dragon*

A knight approaches another dragon and asks his color and type.

Dragon: I am not a red predator.

What is he?

(Hint on page 48)
(Solution on page 59)

P1–3 Two Types*

A knight in armor with lance held in readiness encounters two dragons. He inquires as to the color and type of each.

- A. 1. I am a rational.
-    2. I am grey.
- B.   Dragon A is red.

Considering that one is a rational dragon and one is a predator dragon, what are the color and type of each?

(Hints on page 48)
(Solution on page 59)

P1–4 Two Colors*

A knight in armor confronts two dragons known to be of different colors. They volunteer the following information:

A. 1. Only one of us is a predator.
   2. I am not a predator.
B.   Both of us are predators.

What color and type are each dragon?

(Hints on page 48)
(Solution on page 60)

P1–5 Three Dragons*

Three knights confront three dragons. Each dragon is asked his color and type. They answer below:

A. 1. B is a red predator.
   2. My color is red.
B.   C is a grey rational.
C. 1. A's statements are lies.
   2. B is a grey rational.

What color and type are each of the three dragons?

(Hints on page 49)
(Solution on pages 60–61)

P1–6 Who Speaks the Truth?*

Three dragons are approached by three knights who ask each their color and type. They respond as follows:

A. 1. I am one of the two of us who speak the truth.
    2. B is grey, as am I.
B. 1. C and I always speak the truth.
    2. I am a predator.
C. 1. A and I speak the truth.
    2. I am grey, or else I am the only rational among the three of us.

What are the color and type of each dragon?

(Hints on page 49)
(Solution on page 61)

P1–7 Three and One**

Three large dragons are watching the approach of a lone knight.

A. 1. Here comes a nice plump inexperienced-looking knight.
    2. It is a shame that C is a rational.
B. 1. A's first statement is true.
    2. I am almost sorry to be a rational.
    3. A is a predator.
C. 1. That knight looks lean and battle-tested.
    2. A and B are the same color.
    3. I am a predator.

What color and type are each of the three dragons?

(Hints on page 49)
(Solution on page 62)

P1–8   Four Dragons**

Four knights approach four dragons and inquire as to the color and type of each. The dragons respond as follows:

- A. 1. B and I are the same color and type.
  2. I am grey.
  3. C is a predator.
- B. 1. A's statements are false.
  2. C and I are the same color.
  3. D and I are the same type.
- C. A and D are different colors, but the same type.
- D. A and B are the same color, but different types.

What are the color and type of each dragon?

(Hints on page 49)

(Solution on pages 62–63)

— 2 —
The Adventures of Captain Jean Lafoot, the Pirate

This section chronicles the adventures of the pirate Jean Lafoot and his shipmates. The very name of this ruthless 17th-century buccaneer struck fear in the hearts of many. When Jean Lafoot was a youth, he was obsessed with the mysteries of the sea and the opportunities which it seemed to offer for obtaining great wealth. After he reached his manhood, he obtained a ship, recruited a crew of pirates, and set sail. His objective was to plunder merchant ships wherever he could find them on the open seas.

These puzzles contain conditional statements. Some are valid and some are invalid. The challenge lies in determining which statements you can rely on in your search for solutions.

P2–1 One Overslept*

It was agreed that, while at sea, three of Captain Lafoot's mates would stand watch at night. The three were Black Jack, Long John, and Red Beard. On the first night, one of the three overslept and missed his watch. From the following statements, which mate overslept?

1. If Black Jack stood his watch, then Long John overslept.
2. If Long John stood his watch, then Red Beard overslept.
3. If Black Jack overslept, then Red Beard stood his watch.

(Hint on page 49)

(Solution on pages 63–64)

P2–2 A Chase on the Open Sea*

A merchant ship was sighted and the Captain gave orders to pursue the vessel. After a chase, the merchant ship escaped. From the statements below, how long did the chase last and how did the merchant ship escape?

1. If the merchant ship outran the pirate ship, then the chase lasted all afternoon.
2. If the pirate ship had to stop to mend the mainsail, then the chase lasted all day.
3. If the merchant ship escaped in a fog bank, then the chase lasted 30 minutes or two hours.
4. If the chase lasted 30 minutes or all afternoon, the pirate ship had to stop to mend the mainsail.
5. If the chase lasted two hours or all day, then the merchant ship escaped in a fog bank.

(Hint on pages 49–50)

(Solution on page 64)

P2–3 Buccaneer Quartet*

During a quiet period on the long voyage, Captain Lafoot's four mates entertained themselves by organizing a quartet to sing the lusty buccaneer songs so enjoyed by the pirates. The four forming the quartet were Black Jack, Long John, Red Beard, and Will Kidd. Two sang tenor, one sang baritone, and one sang bass, not necessarily in that order. From the following statements, what part did each sing?

1. If Long John were not one of the tenors, then Black Jack was the baritone.
2. If Red Beard were either the bass or the baritone, then Black Jack was one of the tenors.
3. If Will Kidd were the baritone, then Red Beard was the bass.
4. If Black Jack were not the bass, then he was the baritone.
5. If Will Kidd were not one of the tenors, then Long John was the bass.

(Hint on page 50)
(Solution on page 65)

P2–4 A Sea Serpent*

The Captain spied a merchant vessel and was about to give orders to pursue and attack it. At this moment, a great sea serpent appeared on the port side of the ship and reached for Captain Lafoot. Reacting quickly, the Captain grasped the article nearest him, a belaying pin, and hurled it with all his might into the open maw of the startled monster. It backed down and sank into the depths. By this time the merchant vessel had too great a lead to be overtaken by the pirate ship.

Following the incident there was confusion among the crew members as to the description of the monster. From the statements below, determine the length of the sea serpent (35, 45, or 55 metres) and its color (black, brown, or green).

1. If the sea serpent were not green or if it were not 35 metres long, then it was 55 metres long.
2. If the sea serpent were not 35 metres long or if it were not black, then it was brown.
3. If the sea serpent were not black or if it were not 45 metres long, then it was 55 metres long.
4. If the sea serpent were not 45 metres long or if it were not green, then it was 35 metres long.

(Hint on page 50)
(Solution on page 66)

P2–5 The Island Fish*

A merchant ship was sighted and the pirates were closing in to attack when the giant sea serpent was once again seen close to the pirate ship. Captain Lafoot quickly gave orders to change course and approach what appeared to be an island that would serve as a temporary refuge. What all hands thought to be terra firma was in reality a fish of immense size known as an "island fish." This monster's method was to float on the surface, giving the appearance of an island, and engulf its unsuspecting prey as it came near.

From the following statements, how large was the island fish and what was the outcome of this encounter?

1. If the island fish were one or three leagues long and wide, then a freak cyclone lifted the pirate ship and deposited it out of the reach of the giant fish.
2. If the island fish were not one or four leagues long and wide, then it was so large and slow that it could

not move quickly enough to catch the fleet pirate ship.

3. If the island fish were four leagues long and wide, then it had just consumed three sailing ships and a whale, so was not interested in the pirate ship.

4. If a freak cyclone lifted the pirate ship and deposited it out of the reach of the gigantic fish, then it was three leagues long and wide.

5. If the great fish had just consumed three sailing ships and a whale, so was not interested in the pirate ship, then it was two leagues long and wide.

(Hints on page 50)
(Solution on pages 66–67)

P2–6 The Musket Competition**

During an uneventful period on the open sea, Captain Lafoot and his four mates decided to try their skill with muskets. They placed a target behind the forecastle and, keeping score, they took turns shooting at it. Based on the following statements, determine how each of the five men ranked in the scoring.

1. Captain Lafoot did not rank third unless Red Beard ranked fifth.

2. If Long John ranked second, then Black Jack did not rank either first or third.

3. If Will Kidd did not rank first, then Red Beard ranked second and Long John ranked fourth.

4. If Black Jack did not rank first, then Long John ranked second and Captain Lafoot ranked fourth.

5. If Black Jack did not rank second, then neither did Captain Lafoot nor Red Beard, unless Will Kidd ranked fourth.

(Hints on page 51)
(Solution on pages 67–68)

P2–7 Whose Hair Turned White?**

Captain Lafoot spied a merchant ship and prepared to give chase. Again the pirates were interrupted, as a giant octopus rose from the depths and fastened its powerful tentacles on the pirate ship. Just as the ship was about to be pulled beneath the surface by the octopus, a further menace, the sea serpent, appeared. It attacked the giant octopus, which released the pirate ship, enabling it to flee to safety.

The two monsters were so large and ferocious and the experience so frightening that, of Captain Lafoot and his four mates, the hair on the heads of two of them turned white. From the statements that follow, whose hair turned white?

1. If Will Kidd's hair turned white, then Red Beard's hair turned white.
2. If Black Jack's hair turned white, then Red Beard's hair did not turn white.
3. If Long John's hair turned white, then Captain Lafoot's hair did not turn white.
4. Will Kidd's hair turned white, if Captain Lafoot's hair turned white.

5. If Red Beard's hair turned white, then Long John's hair did not turn white.
6. If Captain Lafoot's hair did not turn white, then Black Jack's hair did not turn white.

(Hints on page 51)
(Solution on pages 68–69)

P2–8 The Sea Serpent Returns***

The ominous sight of the sea serpent, for a fourth time, caused the crew to prepare for battle. As the monster reared its head alongside the ship, all hands fought valiantly. The sea serpent was finally forced to retreat, and it fled the area. Among the Captain and his four mates, two fought with muskets, two fought with cutlasses, and one fought with a dagger. From the statements below, which pirates fought with which weapons?

1. Long John fought using a musket, unless Will Kidd did not fight using a dagger.
2. Black Jack fought using a cutlass, unless Captain Lafoot did not fight using a dagger.
3. If Red Beard fought using a musket, then Long John fought using a cutlass.
4. If Captain Lafoot did not fight using a cutlass, then Red Beard fought using a cutlass and Long John fought using a dagger.
5. Will Kidd fought using a dagger, unless neither Red Beard nor Long John fought using a cutlass.
6. If Will Kidd fought using a musket, then Captain Lafoot did not fight using either a musket or a cutlass.
7. If Black Jack fought using a dagger, then neither Red Beard nor Captain Lafoot fought using a cutlass.

(Hints on page 51)
(Solution on pages 69–71)

— 3 —
The Minikins

When the earth was young, the forests were inhabited by Minikins, who were peace-loving; goblins and trolls, who were not; ogres, who were large, fierce, and belligerent; and giants, who were slow, but mighty.

The puzzles in this section contain fragments of information with just enough information for you to arrive at the correct solution.

P3–1 Narrow Escapes*

It was believed, by others who lived at the time, that the Minikins possessed hidden hoards of gold, and that if one could be captured he could be relieved of a vast treasure. The Minikins, however, were not without defenses. They were small, quick, and camouflaged by the earth-tone coloring of their clothing, and they had an uncanny ability to disappear if one looked away from them for even an instant.

Four Minikins—Ekum, Elfum, Epum, and Eskum—had each had an encounter which resulted in a narrow escape: one from a giant, who moved too slowly; one from two goblins, who got in each other's way; one from an ogre, who blinked; and one from a troll, who slipped and looked down while coming out from under a bridge. Who had which encounter and what was the sequence in which the narrow escapes took place?

1. Neither the first nor the third encounter was with two goblins or an ogre.
2. Eskum's encounter was the third one.
3. The encounter with two goblins came after the encounter with a troll, which was not the first one.
4. Elfum's encounter was not with an ogre.
5. Epum's encounter was the first one.

(Hints on page 52)
(Solutions on pages 71–72)

P3–2 Homes of the Minikins*

The homes of the Minikins were chosen for their seclusion and safety. Among five Minikins—Ekum, Elfum, Epum, Eskum, and Evum—two lived in the hollows of large tree trunks; one lived beneath the roots of a great oak tree; one lived in a hidden hillside cave; and one lived underground with the entrance hidden by a brier patch. Their clothing was of the colors of the earth: two wore green, one wore taupe, one wore brown, and one wore olive.

From the following statements, which lived in which homes and what colors did they wear?

1. The one who wore olive lived beneath the roots of an oak tree.
2. Neither of the two who lived in tree trunks, who were not Ekum or Epum, wore green.
3. Elfum, who did not live under a brier patch, wore green.
4. Neither Ekum nor Evum wore green or brown.

(Hints on page 52)

(Solution on page 72)

P3–3 Musicians*

Elfum and four of his friends among the Minikins gathered together frequently to play their musical instruments. One played a flute, made from a reed; one played a horn, which was a large snail shell; one played a drum, made from a hollow log; one played a rhythm instrument made from a dried gourd; and one played an instrument similar to a lyre, which was made from a curved tree limb with strings made from hair provided by a friendly hedgehog.

Each of four of the five friends lived near one of the others. From the following statements, determine who played which instrument and who lived near which of the others.

1. The one who played the flute lived next door to Eskum.
2. Epum lived adjacent to the one who played the lyre, who was not Eskum.
3. Evum, who did not play the drum, did not live near the one who played the flute.
4. The one who played the horn and the one who played the flute, who was not Ekum, were neighbors.
5. Ekum did not play the gourd or the drum.

(Hints on page 53)
(Solution on page 73)

P3–4 A Skirmish*

Three goblins travelling together chanced to encounter a giant, who was alone, and two ogres, who were walking together. A skirmish broke out among them and all combatants suffered bumps and bruises. Their weapons included three clubs, two staves, and one sling, used for hurling stones.

From the statements below, which ones were the goblins, which ones were the ogres, which one was the giant, and what weapon did each use? (Two names were Rido and Sumo.)

1. No goblin used a staff, nor did Tor.
2. The two ogres used different weapons.
3. The sling was used by one of the goblins.
4. Som, who was not an ogre, used a staff.
5. Opi did not use a club, nor was he a goblin.
6. Tor and Zeb used different weapons.

(Hints on page 53)
(Solution on page 74)

P3-5 Potluck Dinner**

Each lunar period, six Minikins met at Ekum's house and shared a potluck dinner. At one such gathering, one provided acorn soup, one provided mushrooms, one provided forest greens, one provided a variety of nuts, one provided baked fish, and one provided a favorite dessert made from honey, berries, and grain meal. From the following statements, which friends brought which dishes, and what was the sequence of their arrival for the dinner? (Ekum was late getting home, so was not the first to arrive.)

1. Ebum did not bring dessert, mushrooms, or nuts, nor was he the first to arrive.
2. Ekum provided either dessert or nuts, and was not the last to arrive.
3. The one who arrived first, who was not Epum, provided soup.
4. Eskum arrived immediately after Evum, who arrived immediately after Epum.
5. The last to arrive, who was not Eskum, brought the fish.
6. The one who provided mushrooms, who was not Epum, was the third to arrive.
7. The one who arrived immediately after Elfum brought the dessert.

(Hints on page 54)
(Solution on pages 75–76)

P3-6 Athletic Competition**

Athletic ability was admired by the Minikins, and the annual summer competition of athletic events was eagerly anticipated. In one such competition, Ebum, Ekum, Elfum, Epum, and Eskum, and Evum were among the competitors.

Three of them were entered in each of four events, and each of the four events was won by a different one of the six. Based on the statements below, which three entered each of the events and who were the four winners?

1. The winner of the tree climb did not enter the distance run.
2. Ekum entered the distance run and the tree climb.
3. The only one of the four events that Evum did not enter was the log lift.
4. The winner of the spear throw entered one other event.
5. Eskum, who entered the distance run and one other event, and Elfum were both winners.
6. Ebum won the only event that he entered.
7. Epum competed in the tree climb and one other event, which was not the spear throw.

(Hints on pages 54–55)
(Solution on pages 76–77)

P3–7 River Trip**

Nine Minikins, looking for adventure, decided to float down a nearby river on rafts. Three rafts, identified as #1, #2, and #3, were constructed from bundles of reeds tied with vines. A destination down the river was identified and the three rafts were launched.

One of the rafts, passing under a bridge, was pulled underwater by a troll; the three occupants were able to swim to safety. One raft became waterlogged mid-trip and had to be beached. Only one raft arrived at the predetermined destination. Based on the following statements, which three Minikins were on which raft and how did each three fare?

1. Neither Ekum, Elfum, nor Egum was on raft #2, nor were all three on the same raft.

2. Epum and Edum were on the same raft. It was not the one that became waterlogged.
3. Evum, whose raft was not pulled underwater by the troll, was not on the same raft as either Egum or Ekum.
4. Ebum and Ekum were on the same raft. It was not the one that became waterlogged.
5. Egum was on raft #3 along with Eskum.
6. Efrum was not on the raft that was pulled underwater by the troll.

(Hints on page 55)
(Solution on pages 77–78)

P3–8 Autumn Festival and Games**

A festival was held each autumn by the Minikins, and there was much feasting and many contests. At one such time, Ekum, Elfum, Eskum, and Evum each won a first place in one of four events: acorn gathering, dancing, singing, and huckleberry eating; not necessarily in that order. Curiously, each winner also won a second place and a third place in two other of these four events. From the statements below, who won first place, who won second place, and who won third place in each of the four events?

1. The one who placed second in huckleberry eating was third in dancing.
2. The winner of the singing contest placed third in huckleberry eating.
3. Evum did not place first in acorn gathering or dancing.
4. Evum was a close second place behind Eskum in one of the four events.
5. Elfum placed third in singing, but did not place in acorn gathering, and was not first in dancing.

(Hints on page 55)
(Solution on page 79)

— 4 —
Hyperborea

What is generally known about Hyperborea comes to us from Herodotus, who was the first widely known ancient world historian. The name was derived from Borea, the North Wind, and means "beyond the North Wind." The Hyperboreans were a race favored by the gods, particularly Apollo. Theirs was a land of perpetual springtime, disease was nonexistent, and the people lived for a thousand years.

Not so well known are the unique standards of veracity of the inhabitants of Hyperborea. Those Hyperboreans who lived in the southern region, known as Sororeans, always spoke truthfully; those who lived in the northern region, known as Nororeans, always spoke falsely; those who lived in the middle region, known as Midroreans, made statements that were alternatively truthful and false, or false and truthful.

P4–1 Apollo Meets Two*

Apollo occasionally visits the Hyperboreans, in disguise. He would like to establish meaningful dialogue with the inhabitants. The ancient gods were known to have many human characteristics, so it is not surprising that Apollo is having difficulty interpreting their statements.

He engages two inhabitants in conversation, at least one of whom is known to be a Nororean. Apollo inquires as to the standard, or standards, of veracity of the two inhabitants. They respond below:

A. B is not a Nororean.
B. A is a Nororean.

Can you answer Apollo's inquiry?

(Hints on page 56)
(Solution on page 80)

P4–2 Apollo Meets Two More*

The result of this first attempt at communication was not as Apollo had hoped. He addresses two more inhabitants, and asks about their standard, or standards, of veracity. Their answers follow:

A. 1. B and I do not have the same standard of veracity.
   2. I never speak truthfully.
B. 1. A is not a Nororean.
   2. I am not a Nororean.

What group or groups are represented by A and B?

(Hints on page 56)
(Solution on page 80)

P4–3 Delegation from Æthiopia*

Ancient Æthiopia occupied that part of the known world south of Mount Olympus. The Æthiopians wanted to establish diplomatic and trade relationships with Hyperborea, and have sent a delegation to meet with the Hyperboreans.

Inhabitants of Hyperborea belong to three groups according to their standards of veracity: Sororeans, who always speak truthfully; Nororeans, who always speak falsely; and Midroreans, who make statements that are alternately truthful and false, although not necessarily in that order.

The leader of the Æthiopian delegation asks two Hyperboreans about their group or groups. Their statements follow:

A.   I am a Sororean and B is a Nororean.
B. 1. I am either a Nororean or a Midrorean.
     2. A is a Midrorean.

The puzzled Æthiopians return to their land, convinced that establishing any kind of relationship with Hyperborea would not be in their best interests.

What group or groups do A and B represent?

(Hints on page 56)
(Solution on page 81)

P4–4 Who Speaks Truthfully?*

Apollo has been having difficulty communicating with the Hyperboreans. A positive step would be to attempt to identify an inhabitant who always speaks truthfully. He approaches three Hyperboreans and asks who is a Sororean.

The three Hyperboreans are known to be a Sororean, who always speaks truthfully; a Nororean, who always speaks falsely; and a Midrorean, who makes statements that are alternately truthful and false, but which comes first is uncertain. They answer Apollo, as follows:

A. 1. I am the Sororean
   2. B is the Nororean.
B. 1. I am the Sororean.
   2. C is the Midrorean.
C. 1. I am the Sororean.
   2. A is the Midrorean.

Which one is the Sororean, which one is the Nororean, and which one is the Midrorean?

(Hints on page 56)
(Solution on pages 81–82)

P4–5 Who Won the Olive Wreath?*

The major event of the season is the much anticipated Grand Chariot Race. To the winner goes the traditional olive wreath. Three participants in the race, one of whom was the winner, are known to be a Sororean, who always speaks truthfully; a Nororean, who always speaks falsely; and a Midrorean, who makes statements that are alternately truthful and false, but not necessarily in that order.

According to their statements below, which one of them is the Sororean, which is the Nororean, which is the Midrorean, and who won the chariot race?

- A. 1. C crowded me at the last turn, causing me to lose the race.
  - 2. C always tells the truth.
  - 3. C was the winner.
- B. 1. A won the race.
  - 2. C is not the Nororean.
- C. 1. B won the race.
  - 2. I did not crowd A at the last turn, causing him to lose the race.

(Hints on page 56)

(Solution on pages 82–83)

P4–6 The Centaur Prophet*

Centaurs, half human/half horse, were an ancient race that inhabited Mount Pelion, south of Mount Olympus. Among them, Chiron, who was wise and just, became renowned for his skills in music, hunting, medicine and, especially, prophecy. Apollo, recognizing that Chiron the Centaur would be an asset to the Hyperboreans, sent him to dwell in that land.

Chiron seeks to open a conversation with three inhabitants when a fourth Hyperborean happens to walk by. Chiron inquires as to the standards of veracity of the three involved in the conversation and that of the fourth individual.

The three are known to be a Sororean, who always speaks truthfully; a Nororean, who always speaks falsely; and a Midrorean, who makes statements that are alternately truthful and false, although in what order is unknown. As to the fourth inhabitant, little is known. The statements of the three follow:

A. 1. The fourth person is a Sororean, as am I.
   2. Both B and C have been known to speak falsely.
   3. C is less truthful than B or I.
B. 1. The fourth person is a Midrorean.
   2. He does not speak with the same degree of truthfulness that I do.
C. 1. If you were to ask the fourth person, he would claim to be a Nororean.
   2. As A says, he is a Sororean.

At this point, Chiron prophesies that Hyperboreans will always be too strange for him, and he returns to Mount Pelion.

Which of the three is the Sororean, who is the Nororean, who is the Midrorean, and what is the standard of veracity of the fourth person?

(Hints on page 56)
(Solution on page 83)

A Few Were Different

In an isolated land, as Hyperborea was, tradition and conventions were important. The Hyperboreans placed a value on their unusual conventions. There were, however, some who rejected the land's standards of veracity. They were Hyperborea's Outliers.

P4–7 A Chimaera in the Land**

A chimaera had been seen in the land. The forepart of the monster's body was that of a lion and the hind part was that of a dragon. It was, indeed, fearsome to behold. There was much concern, and children and pets were kept indoors. Four Hyperboreans decided that the Chimaera should be confronted and driven from the land.

Hyperboreans are either Sororeans, who always speak truthfully; Nororeans, who always speak falsely; Midroreans who make statements that are alternately truthful and false; or those few Outliers, who do not accept traditional Hyperborean conventions, and whose standards of veracity are different than those of the other three. As to these four inhabitants, each has a different standard of veracity.

The four meet to consider what to do:

A. 1. C is the most experienced in this sort of thing, having defeated a monster before.
   2. The chimaera has the head of a ferocious dragon.
   3. I would volunteer to defeat the chimaera, but my family needs me.
B. 1. D was overheard to claim to be a Nororean.
   2. A does not have a family.
   3. A's second statement is true.
C. 1. I never defeated a monster.
   2. B's first statement is truthful.
   3. We do not really have a chance to defeat the chimaera without outside help.
D. 1. We have a good chance to defeat the monster ourselves.
   2. B's first statement is truthful.
   3. A's second statement is truthful.

The chimaera was apparently just passing through the land, as it was not seen again.

Can you determine the standard of veracity of each of the four Hyperboreans?

(Hints on page 57)
(Solution on page 84)

P4–8 Who Is the Outlier?***

The number of Outliers among the Hyperboreans is increasing. It seems that every small group of inhabitants includes an Outlier. Of the four Hyperboreans who make statements below, one is a Sororean, who always speaks truthfully; one is a Nororean, who always speaks falsely; one is a Midrorean, who makes statements that are alternately truthful and false; and one is an Outlier, whose standard of veracity is different than the standards of the other three. They make the following statements:

- A. 1. C is not more truthful than I am.
  2. D is not the Sororean.
  3. B is not the Outlier.
- B. 1. C is less truthful than I am.
  2. D is the Midrorean.
  3. A is the Outlier.
- C. 1. A is the Nororean.
  2. B always tells the truth.
  3. I am the Outlier.
- D. 1. B is less truthful than I am.
  2. A is not the Outlier.
  3. A is more truthful than C.

Which one is the Sororean, which one is the Nororean, which one is the Midrorean, and which one is the Outlier?

(Hints on page 57)

(Solution on pages 85–86)

P4–9 Some Are More Equal Than Others***

In the land of Hyperborea all are considered equal. However, Hyperboreans lived for a thousand years, and old age was associated with rank and was venerated. It was not, therefore, surprising that some tended to exaggerate their ages.

Five workers, a blacksmith, a fisherman, an olive picker and two shepherds, are engaged in conversation. Two are known to be Sororeans, who always speak truthfully; one is

known to be a Nororean, who always speaks falsely; and one is known to be a Midrorean, who makes statements that are alternately truthful and false, although the order is uncertain. The fifth is an Outlier, who does not adhere to any of the Hyperborean traditional standards of veracity. They make the following statements:

Epimetheus:
1. The Olive Festival is the most important event of the season.
2. The fisherman is the youngest among the five of us.
3. I am the blacksmith.

Gordius:
1. I am not the olive picker.
2. At least one of Epimetheus' statements is true.
3. Iphis is not the fisherman.
4. I am the oldest among the five of us.

Iphis:
1. Vertumnus is the oldest among us.
2. I am the second oldest among us.
3. Picking olives requires great skill and I do it well.
4. Gordius is not the Midrorean.

Phaeton:
1. The blacksmith is the third oldest among us.
2. Epimetheus' statements are not all false.
3. I am the older of the two shepherds.

Vertumnus:
1. I am the oldest of the five of us.
2. I am a shepherd.
3. Phaeton's second statement is true.

Which ones are the Sororeans; which one is the Nororean; which one is the Midrorean; and which one is the Outlier? What is the job of each, and what is their rank in age?

(Hints on page 57)
(Solution on pages 86–87)

Nonsense

Here are five puzzles that are different. They may seem absurd and may not rely on any facts of which we have knowledge. There is logic in them, however, if you can assume that the statements are valid. Can you uncover the inference in each puzzle?

P5–1 Rabbits Play Hockey*

1. Some alligators carry umbrellas in the shower.
2. Only those that know that flying fish live in the trees prefer caramel candy to chocolate.
3. Certain days are set aside for alligators to watch rabbits play hockey.
4. Some large reptiles are steeplechasers.
5. Only steeplechasers can watch hockey games.
6. Those alligators that carry umbrellas in the shower know that flying fish live in the trees.
7. Those that prefer chocolate to caramel candy cannot be steeplechasers.
8. Steeplechasers are vegetarians.

What inference can you draw from the above statements?

(Hints on page 57)
(Solution on page 88)

P4–2 Gorillas Enjoy Ballet*

1. Gorillas are the only animals that enjoy ballet.
2. All animals can fly to Mars.
3. Scotch broom blooms every Thursday all over Mars.
4. Only those few animals that do not play solitaire are immune to hay fever.
5. No animal that travels in leaky rowboats ever has the penultimate word in a verbal discourse

6. Scotch broom in bloom is what gives animals severe hay fever.
7. Those that do not handle hot ice cubes travel to town in leaky rowboats.
8. All animals that have the penultimate word in a verbal discourse play solitaire.
9. No animal that enjoys ballet handles hot ice cubes.

What can you infer from these statements?

(Hints on page 57)
(Solution on page 88)

P5–3 No Books in the Second Solar Period of the Week*

1. It is the law that books may never be read in the second solar period of the week.
2. Curly-maned mountain lions never get snowed upon while sailing.
3. When it rains it always snows.
4. Animals that wear green shoes to church go sailing in the first lunar period of the season.
5. You cannot take the fourth solar period of the week off if you do not obey the book law at all times.
6. Those who obey the law earn extra credits.
7. It always rains in the fourth solar period of each week in the first lunar period of the season.
8. Green shoes are what curly-maned mountain lions always wear to church.
9. Curly-maned mountain lions receive the maximum number of credits.

What can you infer from these statements?

(Hints on page 57)
(Solution on page 89)

P5–4 Sentient Beings*

1. Huckleberry mush is delivered universally by sailing ships.
2. Numismatists understand about nutrition.
3. Aliens from other galaxies enjoy watching fish ski.
4. Those who can leap high don't do it often.
5. No one who is especially fond of chess is not also a numismatist.
6. All sentient beings enjoy huckleberry mush.
7. Those who know that certain types of fish ski are avid chess players.
8. Infrequent leapers like their food chilled.
9. Anyone who knows about nutrition is capable of leaping tall buildings.

On the assumption that the above statements are valid, what inference can be drawn?

(Hints on page 57)
(Solution on page 89)

P5–5 Neighbors Make Good Fences**

1. Neighbors make good fences.
2. Purple popcorn can only be eaten in specially designated places.
3. No angler can be considered a true angler who is not a striped otter that does not fish with other than woolly worms.
4. No mammal that has not attended the Hayberry Island Culinary Institute can be a certified chef.
5. No mammal stands on fences.
6. Graduates of the Hayberry Island Culinary Institute make purple popcorn.
7. Only true anglers receive invitations to good fences.
8. Platypuses that are neighbors are certified chefs.
9. Good fences are the places to sit and eat purple popcorn by invitation.
10. Striped otters have a variety of fishing lures from which to select.
11. Platypuses do not eat sitting down.

What inference can you draw from these statements?

(Hints on page 57)
(Solution on page 90)

— 6 —
The Land of Liars

In the Land of Liars the inhabitants are all liars, but not all the time. There are those who speak the truth in the morning and lie in the afternoon. The inhabitants in this group are known as Amtrus. There are also those who speak the truth in the afternoon and lie in the morning. The inhabitants in this group are known as Pemtrus.

Your challenge in each puzzle is to identify the Amtrus and the Pemtrus, and to determine if it is morning or afternoon.

P6–1 Two Inhabitants*

Two inhabitants are known to be an Amtru, who speaks the truth only in the morning, and a Pemtru, who speaks the truth only in the afternoon. A makes the following statement:

A. B is the Amtru.

Is it morning or afternoon; which one is the Amtru and which one is the Pemtru?

(Hints on page 57)
(Solution on page 90)

P6–2 Two Inhabitants Again*

Two inhabitants are asked the time of day. The two are known to be an Amtru, who speaks the truth only in the morning, and a Pemtru, who speaks the truth only in the afternoon. They respond, as follows:

A. It is morning.
B. A is the Pemtru.

Is it morning or afternoon; which one is the Amtru and which one is the Pemtru?

(Hints on page 57)
(Solution on page 91)

P6–3 Two Inhabitants Once Again*

This time, little is known as to the group or groups of the two individuals who make the statements that follow.

A. B and I are Amtrus.
B. A is a Pemtru.

Is it morning or evening; and what group or groups do the two speakers represent?

(Hints on page 58)
(Solution on pages 91–92)

P6–4 Three Inhabitants*

This time three inhabitants are approached. Two are known to be Amtrus, and one is known to be a Pemtru. They volunteer the following statements:

A. B is the Pemtru.
B. C is an Amtru.
C. A is the Pemtru.

Is it morning or afternoon; which two are the Amtrus and which one is the Pemtru?

(Hints on page 58)
(Solution on page 92)

P6–5 Three Inhabitants Again**

Three inhabitants are asked the time of day. Two are Pemtrus and one is an Amtru. They respond as follows:

A. If asked, B would claim it is morning.
B. If asked, C would claim it is morning.
C. If asked, A would claim it is afternoon.

Is it morning or afternoon; which inhabitants belong to which groups?

(Hints on page 58)

(Solution on pages 92–93)

P6–6 Morning and Afternoon**

It is late morning. Six inhabitants of the Land of Liars are engaged in a conversation, as follows:

A. I wish it would stop raining.
B. It has not started to rain.
C. I agree with B's statement.

At this point in the conversation, the clock strikes 12:00 noon.

D. B is a Pemtru.
E. A and I are not from the same group.
F. A and D are from the same group.

Which one or ones are Amtrus; which one or ones are Pemtrus; and which one or ones can we not tell about from these statements?

(Hints on page 58)
(Solution on pages 93–94)

P6–7 Four Inhabitants***

Four inhabitants make the statements below. As to their group or groups, little is known except that B and C are not both Amtrus.

A. If asked, B would say that he and D belong to the same group.
B. If asked, D would say that he and A do not belong to the same group.
C. A and I are both Pemtrus.
D. If asked, A would say that he and C do not belong to the same group.

Is it morning or afternoon, and to what group or groups do the four speakers belong?

(Hints on page 58)
(Solution on pages 94–95)

H1 THE DRAGONS OF LIDD

H1–1 One Dragon Could the dragon be a grey predator? If not, why not?

H1–2 Another Dragon Is the statement true or false?

For puzzles **1–3** to **1–8**, construct a diagram with color and type on one axis, and listing each speaker on the other axis, as illustrated below:

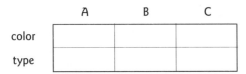

	A	B	C
color			
type			

As you draw conclusions, indicate red or grey and rational or predator in the diagram.

H1–3 Two Types: Consider that one is a rational, and one is a predator. If A's first statement is a lie, what is he?

H1–4 Two Colors: Consider that one is red and one is grey. If A has told the truth, what is he? How about B?

H1–5 Three Dragons What are the possibilities for B? Compare each possibility with the statements of the other two dragons.

H1–6 Who Speaks the Truth? If A's statements are true, what type is he? How about B?

H1–7 Three and One What are the possibilities, considering A's, B's, and C's first statements?

H1–8 Four Dragons What can you conclude from A's and B's first statements?

H2 THE ADVENTURES OF CAPTAIN JEAN LAFOOT, THE PIRATE

H2–1 One Overslept Construct a diagram, such as below. Mark a plus or minus sign as you determine whether a statement is valid or not.

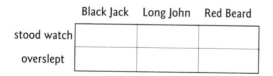

	Black Jack	Long John	Red Beard
stood watch			
overslept			

If the hypothesis in statement 3 is valid, what does this say about Long John?

H2–2 A Chase on the Open Sea A diagram, such as below, will be helpful. Mark a plus or minus sign as you draw conclusions as to whether or not statements are valid.

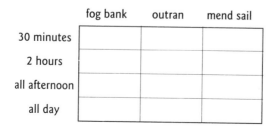

	fog bank	outran	mend sail
30 minutes			
2 hours			
all afternoon			
all day			

Compare statements 1 and 4. What does this tell you about the validity of the assumption in statement 1?

H2–3 Buccaneer Quartet Construct a diagram, as below:

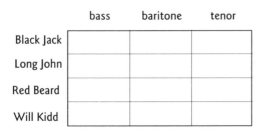

	bass	baritone	tenor
Black Jack			
Long John			
Red Beard			
Will Kidd			

Consider statement 4. Could Black Jack be one of the tenors?

H2–4 A Sea Serpent A diagram, as below, will be helpful:

	black	brown	green
35 metres			
45 metres			
55 metres			

Consider statement 1. If the serpent was 45 metres long, what color would it have to be?

H2–5 The Island Fish Prepare a diagram, such as follows:

	ate 3 merchant ships & a whale	pirate ship too small to notice	cyclone lifted ship to safety	fish too slow to catch ship
1 league long/wide				
2 leagues long/wide				
3 leagues long/wide				
4 leagues long/wide				

Consider statements 1 and 4. Could the island fish be one league long and wide?

H2–6 The Musket Competition   Construct a diagram, such as below:

	1st	2nd	3rd	4th	5th
Black Jack					
Captain Lafoot					
Long John					
Red Beard					
Will Kidd					

Consider statement 3. Could Will Kidd have ranked second or fourth?

H2–7 Whose Hair Turned White?   A simple diagram, such as below, will be useful.

	Black Jack	Captain Lafoot	Long John	Red Beard	Will Kidd
hair turned white					

Consider statement 3. If the assumption is valid, Long John's hair turned white. If so, which other pirates' hair could have turned white?

H2–8 The Sea Serpent Returns   Prepare the following diagram:

	cutlass	dagger	musket
Black Jack			
Captain Lafoot			
Long John			
Red Beard			
Will Kidd			

Consider statement 4. Could Captain Lafoot have fought using a dagger?

H3 THE MINIKINS

H3–1 Narrow Escapes Construct a composite diagram, as below, and mark a plus or minus sign as you confirm or rule out a conclusion.

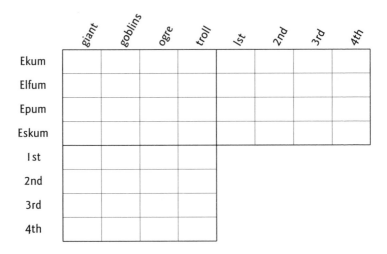

From statements 1 and 3, which encounter was first?

H3–2 Homes of the Minikins A diagram, such as below, will be helpful.

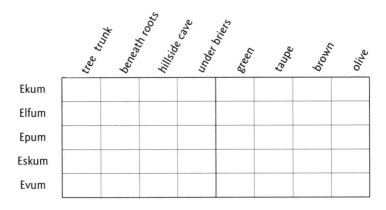

From statements 1, 2 and 3, where did Elfum live?

H3–3 Musicians Construct a diagram, such as the following:

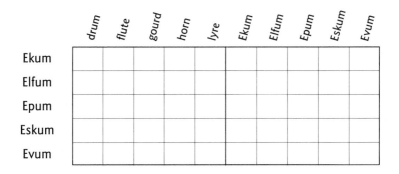

	drum	flute	gourd	horn	lyre	Ekum	Elfum	Epum	Eskum	Evum
Ekum										
Elfum										
Epum										
Eskum										
Evum										

From statements 1 and 4, what instrument did Eskum play?

H3–4 A Skirmish Prepare a composite diagram, such as below:

	giant	goblin	ogre	club	sling	staff
Opi						
Rido						
Som						
Sumo						
Tor						
Zeb						
club						
sling						
staff						

From statements 1 and 4, what was Som?

H3–5 Potluck Dinner A composite diagram, such as below, will help:

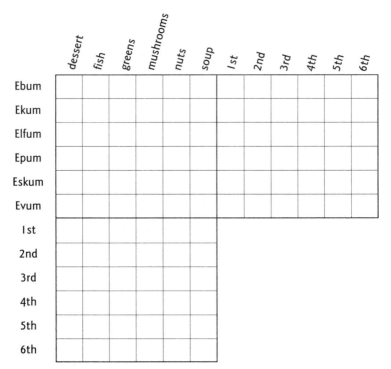

From statements 1, 3, and 4, who brought the soup? Consider that Ekum was late getting home, so was not the first to arrive.

H3–6 Athletic Competition A diagram, such as below, will be helpful:

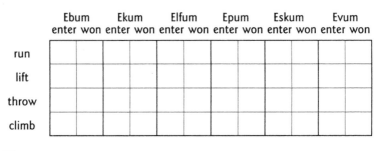

Consider that of the six, only three entered any one of the four events and each event was won by a different Minikin. From statements 2, 3, and 5, which three entered the distance run?

H3–7 River Trip Two diagrams, such as below, will be helpful:

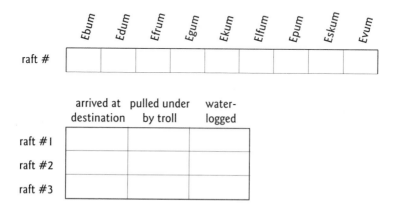

Consider statement 1. What are the possible rafts for Ekum, Elfum, and Egum? What do statements 3, 4, and 5 add?

H3–8 Autumn Festival and Games Prepare a diagram, such as the following:

Consider that each of the four won a first, second, and third place. From statement 5, which event did Elfum win?

	acorn gathering			dancing			singing			huckleberry eating		
	1st	2nd	3rd	1st	2nd	3rd	1st	2nd	3rd	1st	2nd	3rd
Ekum												
Elfum												
Eskum												
Evum												

H4 HYPERBOREA

For each of the puzzles in this section, prepare a diagram depicting the speakers on one axis and Sororean, Nororean, and Midrorean on the other axis, as illustrated below. (For puzzles 4–7, 4–8, and 4–9, add Outlier.) As you draw conclusions, mark plus or minus in the appropriate spaces.

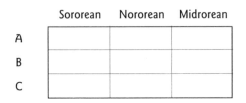

	Sororean	Nororean	Midrorean
A			
B			
C			

H4–1 Apollo Meets Two Could A be a Nororean?

H4–2 Apollo Meets Two More Could A's second statement be truthful?

H4–3 Delegation from Æthiopia Consider that if either part of B's first statement is true, the statement is true.

H4–4 Who Speaks Truthfully? Could B be the Nororean, as A states?

H4–5 Who Won the Olive Wreath? One of the three Hyperboreans is the Sororean. Could it be A? If not, why not?

H4–6 The Centaur Prophet Consider which one of A, B, and C is the Sororean. What are the implications of A's third statement in relationship to C's second statement?

Puzzles **4–7**, **4–8**, and **4–9** involve an additional complication: the Outlier. To be different from a Sororean, a Nororean, or a Midrorean, an Outlier must make two consecutive statements that are both truthful or both false and one statement that is false or truthful, not necessarily in that order.

H4–7 A Chimaera in the Land Since four standards of veracity are represented, one is a Sororean, one is a Nororean, one is a Midrorean, and one is an Outlier. Consider the implications of B's first statement being false, recognizing that one of the four is a Sororean. Also consider A's second statement; is it truthful?

H4–8 Who Is the Outlier? Consider the possibility of A being the Outlier, as indicated by B's third statement. If not, consider the possibility of B being the Outlier; how about speaker D?

H4–9 Some Are More Equal Than Others Consider that there are two Sororeans, one Nororean, one Midrorean, and one Outlier. Could Phaeton's second statement be false? If so, what does this tell us about the statements by the other speakers?

H5 NONSENSE

Each of the five puzzles in this section can be solved by grouping the statements that appear to be related. This step will help lead to the inference in each puzzle.

H6 THE LAND OF LIARS

For each puzzle, prepare a diagram indicating Amtru and Pemtru on one axis and listing each speaker on the other axis. Assume either morning or afternoon and test the consistency of the statements against your assumption. As you test your assumptions look for contradictions.

H6–1 Two Inhabitants Consider that one is an Amtru and one is a Pemtru. A claims that B is the Amtru. What are the possibilities for A?

H6–2 Two Inhabitants Again Consider that one is an Amtru and one is a Pemtru. Could A be the Pemtru?

H6–3 Two Inhabitants Once Again Consider A's statement. What are the alternatives for A?

H6–4 Three Inhabitants Consider that two are Amtrus and one is a Pemtru. If it is afternoon and A's statement is true, what does that make A? Consider B and C.

H6–5 Three Inhabitants Again Consider that there are two Pemtrus and one Amtru. Assume C is an Amtru, both in the morning and the afternoon. Assume C is a Pemtru, both in the morning and the afternoon. Follow the implications for A and B. Only one of the alternatives is possible.

H6–6 Morning and Afternoon From E's statement, what can we conclude about A?

H6–7 Four Inhabitants Consider that B and C are not both Amtrus. Also, consider C's statement. What are the possibilities for C and A?

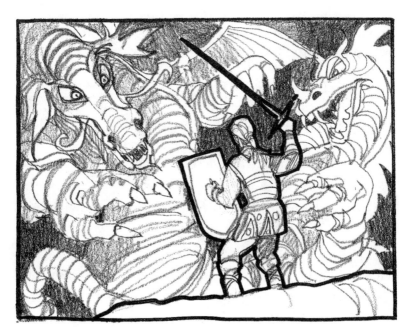

Solutions

S1–1 ONE DRAGON

CONSIDERATIONS
If the dragon were a red predator or a grey rational, he would tell the truth. The dragon lied, and since he is not a grey predator, he is a red rational.
SUMMARY SOLUTION: The dragon is a red rational.

S1–2 ANOTHER DRAGON

CONSIDERATIONS
If the dragon were lying, this would make him a red predator. However, red predators always tell the truth. Therefore, he told the truth. Therefore, he must be a grey rational.
SUMMARY SOLUTION: He is a grey rational dragon.

S1–3 TWO TYPES

CONSIDERATIONS
Consider that one is a predator dragon and one is a rational dragon.

If A's first statement is a lie, he is a grey predator. However, if his first statement is a lie, the second statement is also. Since he claims to be grey, he must be a grey rational dragon. B has lied. Therefore, he is a grey predator.

	A	B
color	grey	grey
type	rational	predator

SUMMARY SOLUTION

    A. grey rational
    B. grey predator

S1–4 TWO COLORS

CONSIDERATIONS

Consider that one is red and one is grey.

Assume that A's statements are truthful. If so, A is a grey rational dragon. If so, B must have lied, and is a grey predator. However, since they are of two colors, A's statements are false; A is a grey predator. B's statement is true; B is a red predator.

	A	B
color	grey	red
type	predator	predator

SUMMARY SOLUTION

    A. grey predator
    B. red predator

S1–5 THREE DRAGONS

CONSIDERATIONS

If B has lied, he must be a red rational or a grey predator. If so, C is not a grey rational. C could be a grey predator, a red rational, or a red predator. However, since his second statement, that B is a grey rational, would be false, his first statement is also false. If so, A is either a grey rational or a red predator. In either case, A's first statement would be true. B would be a red predator. This is inconsistent with our assumption that B has lied.

Therefore, B's statement is true; C is a grey rational, as is B. A, whose statements are false, is a grey predator.

	A	B	C
color	grey	grey	grey
type	predator	rational	rational

SUMMARY SOLUTION

   A. grey predator
   B. grey rational
   C. grey rational

S1–6 WHO SPEAKS THE TRUTH?

CONSIDERATIONS

Assume that A's first statement is true. If so, from A's second statement, A must be a grey rational, and B is a grey rational or a grey predator. However, B's second statement confirms that he is a predator, and grey predators always lie. Therefore, if A's second statement is true, so is B's second statement, which is inconsistent with A's first statement. Therefore, B must be a red rational or a red predator, and A's statements are false. A could be a red rational or a grey predator.

Since we know A is a liar, from C's first statement C is also a liar. If either part of C's second statement is true, the statement is true. Therefore, both parts must be false. From C's second statement, C is a red rational, and at least one of A and B is also a rational.

From B's first statement, B is also a liar. Therefore, from B's second statement, B is a red rational. Therefore, A must be a grey predator.

	A	B	C
color	grey	red	red
type	predator	rational	rational

SUMMARY SOLUTION

   A. grey predator
   B. red rational
   C. red rational

S1–7 THREE AND ONE

CONSIDERATIONS

B's first statement agrees with A's first statement, with which C's first statement disagrees. We can conclude that, if C's first statement is true, A's and B's first statements are both false; and if A's and B's first statements are true, C's first statement is a lie. (From the first statements alone, it is possible that all three are false. However, consideration of A's second statement and C's third statement reinforces the conclusion.)

Assume that C's second statement is true. If so, A and B are both either red rationals or grey predators. However, if so, this would make either B's second statement or third statement true.

Therefore, C's statements are false. C, who claims to be a predator, must be a red rational. B, whose statements are true, is a grey rational and A is a red predator.

	A	B	C
color	red	grey	red
type	predator	rational	rational

SUMMARY SOLUTION

- A. red predator
- B. grey rational
- C. red rational

S1–8 FOUR DRAGONS

CONSIDERATIONS

A's statements are false, otherwise B's first statement would agree with A's first statement. A is not grey. He must be a red rational. B's statements are true, since he correctly states that A's statements are false. B is a grey rational or a red predator.

If D's statement is false, A and B must be different colors

and the same type (B would be a grey rational), the same color and the same type (B would be a red rational), or different colors and different types (B would be a grey predator). Since we know that B is a grey rational or a red predator, the only possibility for B would be a grey rational. If so, from B's third statement, D would be a red rational. From B's second statement, C would be grey. Since A and D would both be red rationals, C's statement would be false; C would be a grey predator. However, this agrees with A's first statement, which we know to be false.

Therefore, D's statement is true: B is a red predator as is D (from B's third statement). C's statement is false (A and D are not different colors). C is a red rational (from B's second statement).

	A	B	C	D
color	red	red	red	red
type	rational	predator	rational	predator

SUMMARY SOLUTION

- A. red rational
- B. red predator
- C. red rational
- D. red predator

S2–1 ONE OVERSLEPT

CONSIDERATIONS

From statement 3, if Black Jack overslept, Red Beard stood his watch. If so, Long John must have stood his watch. However, from statement 2, if Long John stood his watch Red Beard overslept. Therefore, the hypothesis in statement 3 is not valid: Black Jack did not oversleep.

Therefore, from statement 1, since we know that Black Jack stood his watch, Long John was the one who overslept.

	Black Jack	Long John	Red Beard
stood watch	+	−	+
overslept	−	+	−

SUMMARY SOLUTION Long John overslept.

S2–2 A CHASE ON THE OPEN SEA

CONSIDERATIONS

From statement 1, if the merchant ship outran the pirate ship, the chase lasted all afternoon. However, from statement 4, if the chase lasted all afternoon, the pirate ship had to stop to mend the mainsail. Therefore, the assumption in statement 1 is invalid: the merchant ship did not outrun the pirate ship.

The assumption in statement 2, that the pirate ship had to stop to mend the mainsail, relies on the chase lasting all day. From statement 5, if the chase lasted all day, the merchant ship escaped in a fog bank. Therefore, the pirate ship did not stop to mend the mainsail.

Our conclusions so far are as follows:

	fog bank	outran	mend sail
30 minutes		−	−
2 hours		−	−
all afternoon		−	−
all day		−	−

The merchant ship escaped in a fog bank; and, from statements 5 and 3, the chase lasted two hours.

SUMMARY SOLUTION The merchant ship escaped in a fog bank and the chase lasted two hours.

S2–3 BUCCANEER QUARTET

CONSIDERATIONS

From statement 4, Black Jack was either the bass or the baritone; he was not one of the tenors. From statement 2, if Red Beard were either the bass or the baritone, Black Jack was one of the tenors. Therefore, since we know that Black Jack was not one of the tenors, Red Beard was one of the tenors.

From statement 3, if Will Kidd was the baritone, Red Beard was the bass. Since we know that Red Beard was one of the tenors, Will Kidd was not the baritone. From statement 5, if Will Kidd were not one of the tenors, Long John was the bass. Therefore, Will Kidd was not the bass. Therefore, Will Kidd was one of the tenors.

Considerations, at this point, are:

	bass	baritone	tenor
Black Jack			–
Long John			–
Red Beard	–	–	+
Will Kidd	–	–	+

From statement 1, if Long John were not one of the tenors, Black Jack was the baritone. Since we know that Long John was not one of the tenors, Black Jack was the baritone and Long John was the bass. (Even though the hypothesis in statement 5 was invalid, this does not preclude Long John from being the bass.)

SUMMARY SOLUTION

Black Jack	baritone
Long John	bass
Red Beard	tenor
Will Kidd	tenor

S2-4 A SEA SERPENT

CONSIDERATIONS

If the assumption in statement 1 were valid, the sea serpent was 55 metres long. If the assumption were invalid, the sea serpent was either 35 metres long or 45 metres long and green. Therefore, the sea serpent was not 45 metres long and brown or 45 metres long and black.

If the assumption in statement 4 were valid, the sea serpent was 35 metres long. If the assumption were invalid, the sea serpent was either 45 metres long or 55 metres long and green. Therefore, the sea serpent was not 55 metres long and brown or 55 metres long and black.

If the assumption in statement 2 were valid, the sea serpent was brown. If the assumption were invalid, the sea serpent was either black or green and 35 metres long. Therefore, the sea serpent was not green and 45 metres long or green and 55 metres long.

Our conclusions, at this point, are:

	black	brown	green
35 metres			
45 metres	–	–	–
55 metres	–	–	–

From statement 3, since we know that the sea serpent was 35 metres long, the assumption was invalid, and the color was neither green nor brown; it was black.

SUMMARY SOLUTION

The sea serpent was 35 metres long and black.

S2-5 THE ISLAND FISH

CONSIDERATIONS

From statement 1, if the island fish were one or three

leagues long and wide, the ship was carried away by a cyclone. From statement 4, if the ship were carried away by a cyclone, the island fish was three leagues long and wide. Therefore, we can conclude that the monster fish was not one league long and wide.

From statement 3, if the island fish were four leagues long and wide, it had just consumed three sailing ships. However, from statement 5, if the island fish had just consumed three sailing ships, it was two leagues long and wide. Therefore, it was not four leagues long and wide.

At this point, our conclusions are:

	ate 3 merchant ships & a whale	pirate ship too small to notice	cyclone lifted ship to safety	fish too slow to catch ship
I league long/wide	–	–	–	–
2 leagues long/wide				
3 leagues long/wide				
4 leagues long/wide	–	–	–	–

From statement 2, since we know that the island fish was not one or four leagues long and wide, it was too slow to catch the fleet pirate ship. Therefore, from statement 1, it was not three leagues long and wide, so was two leagues long and wide.

SUMMARY SOLUTION
The island fish was two leagues long and wide; and the outcome was that it was too large and slow to catch the fleet pirate ship.

S2–6 THE MUSKET COMPETITION

CONSIDERATIONS

From statement 3, Will Kidd did not rank second or fourth. From statement 4, Black Jack did not rank second or fourth. From statement 5, since Black Jack did not rank second and Will Kidd did not rank fourth, neither Captain Lafoot nor Red Beard ranked second. Therefore, Long John must have ranked second.From statement 2, since Long John ranked second, Black Jack did not rank first or third. Therefore, Black Jack ranked fifth.

Our conclusions, so far, are:

	lst	2nd	3rd	4th	5th
Black Jack	–	–	–	–	+
Captain Lafoot		–			
Long John	–	+	–	–	
Red Beard		–			
Will Kidd		–		–	

From statement 1, since Red Beard did not rank fifth, Captain Lafoot did not rank third. From statement 3, since Red Beard did not rank second, and Long John did not rank fourth, Will Kidd ranked first. Therefore, Captain Lafoot ranked fourth. Therefore, Red Beard ranked third.

SUMMARY SOLUTION

Black Jack	fifth
Captain Lafoot	fourth
Long John	second
Red Beard	third
Will Kidd	first

S2–7 WHOSE HAIR TURNED WHITE?

CONSIDERATIONS

According to statement 3, if Long John's hair turned white, Captain Lafoot's hair did not turn white. If the assumption is valid, one and one only of the hair of either Black Jack, Red Beard, or Will Kidd turned white. However, from statement 5, if Red Beard's hair turned white, Long John's hair did not turn white; from statement 1, if Will Kidd's hair turned white, Red Beard's hair turned white; and from statement 6, if Captain Lafoot's hair did not turn white, neither did Black Jack's. Therefore, Long John's hair did not turn white.

According to statement 2, if Black Jack's hair turned white, Red Beard's hair did not turn white. If the assumption is valid, one and only one of the hair of either Long John, Captain Lafoot or Will Kidd turned white. However, we know that Long John's hair did not turn white; from statement 1, if Will Kidd's hair turned white, so did Red Beard's hair and, from statement 4, if Captain Lafoot's hair turned white, so did Will Kidd's. Therefore, Black Jack's hair did not turn white.

Our conclusions, so far:

	Black Jack	Captain Lafoot	Long John	Red Beard	Will Kidd
hair turned white	–		–		

From statement 4, if Captain Lafoot's hair turned white, Will Kidd's hair turned white. However, from statement 1, Will Kidd's hair turning white depends on Red Beard's hair turning white. Therefore, Captain Lafoot's hair did not turn white.

SUMMARY SOLUTION The hair of Red Beard and Will Kidd turned white.

S2–8 THE SEA SERPENT RETURNS

CONSIDERATIONS
From statement 4, if the Captain did not use a cutlass, Long John was the one who used a dagger. Therefore, we can conclude that the Captain did not use a dagger; he must have used a musket or a cutlass. From statement 2, since the Captain did not use a dagger, Black Jack did not use a

cutlass. From statement 7, if Black Jack used a dagger, neither Red Beard nor the Captain used a cutlass. However, from statement 4, a cutlass was used by either of these two. Therefore, Black Jack did not use a dagger; he must have used a musket.

From statement 6, if Will Kidd used a musket, the Captain did not use a musket or cutlass. However, since we know that the Captain used either a musket or a cutlass, Will Kidd did not use a musket; he used a cutlass or a dagger. From statement 5, Will Kidd used a dagger, unless neither Red Beard nor Long John used a cutlass. However, if Will Kidd used a dagger, either Red Beard or Long John must have used a cutlass, since Black Jack is one of the two who used a musket. Therefore, Will Kidd used a cutlass. From statement 1, since Will Kidd used a cutlass, Long John did not use a musket.

At this point our conclusions are as follows:

	cutlass	dagger	musket
Black Jack	−	−	+
Captain Lafoot		−	
Long John			−
Red Beard			
Will Kidd	+	−	−

Among Long John, Red Beard, and Captain Lafoot, either Red Beard or the Captain used a musket, one of the three used a cutlass, and either Long John or Red Beard used a dagger. If the Captain used a cutlass, Red Beard must have used a musket. However, from statement 3, if Red Beard used a musket, Long John used a cutlass. Therefore, Red Beard did not use a musket. Therefore, Captain Lafoot used a musket. From statement 4, Red Beard used a cutlass and Long John used a dagger.

SUMMARY SOLUTION

Black Jack	musket
Captain Lafoot	musket
Long John	dagger
Red Beard	cutlass
Will Kidd	cutlass

S3–1 NARROW ESCAPES

CONSIDERATIONS

From statement 5, Epum's encounter was the first one. From statements 1 and 3, the first encounter was not with two goblins, an ogre, or a troll. Therefore, Epum's encounter was with a giant.

From statement 2, Eskum's encounter was the third one. From statement 1, since the third encounter was not with two goblins or an ogre, it must have been with a troll.

From statement 4, Elfum's encounter was not with an ogre. Therefore, it was with two goblins, and Ekum's encounter was with an ogre. From statement 3, since the encounter with two goblins was after the encounter with a troll, it was the fourth one, and the encounter with an ogre was the second one.

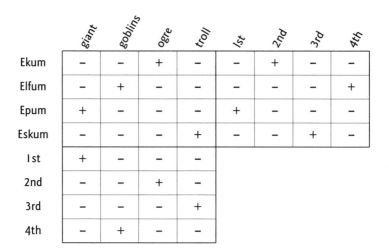

	giant	goblins	ogre	troll	1st	2nd	3rd	4th
Ekum	−	−	+	−	−	+	−	−
Elfum	−	+	−	−	−	−	−	+
Epum	+	−	−	−	+	−	−	−
Eskum	−	−	−	+	−	−	+	−
1st	+	−	−	−				
2nd	−	−	+	−				
3rd	−	−	−	+				
4th	−	+	−	−				

SUMMARY SOLUTION

Ekum	ogre	2nd
Elfum	goblins	4th
Epum	giant	1st
Eskum	troll	3rd

S3–2 HOMES OF THE MINIKINS

CONSIDERATIONS

From statements 3, 1, and 2, Elfum wore green, and did not live under a brier patch, beneath the roots of an oak tree, or in a tree trunk. Therefore, Elfum lived in a hillside cave. From statement 2, the two who lived in tree trunks were Eskum and Evum. One of them wore taupe and the other wore brown. Since, from statement 4, Evum did not wear brown, he wore taupe and Eskum wore brown. From statement 1, Ekum, who wore olive, lived beneath the roots of an oak tree. Epum lived under a brier patch and wore green.

	tree trunk	beneath roots	hillside cave	under briers	green	taupe	brown	olive
Ekum	–	+	–	–	–	–	–	+
Elfum	–	–	+	–	+	–	–	–
Epum	–	–	–	+	+	–	–	–
Eskum	+	–	–	–	–	–	+	–
Evum	+	–	–	–	–	+	–	–

SUMMARY SOLUTION

Ekum	beneath roots	olive
Elfum	hillside cave	green
Epum	under briers	green
Eskum	tree trunk	brown
Evum	tree trunk	taupe

CONSIDERATIONS

From statements 1, 2, 3, and 4, neither Eskum, Epum, Evum, nor Ekum played the flute. Therefore, Elfum played the flute. From statements 1 and 4, Eskum played the horn, and he and Elfum were neighbors.

From statements 3 and 5, neither Evum nor Ekum played the drum. Therefore, since we know that neither Elfum nor Eskum played the drum, the drum was played by Epum. Since, from statement 5, Ekum did not play the gourd, he played the lyre, and Evum played the gourd.

From statement 2, Epum and Ekum, who played the lyre, were neighbors. Therefore, Evum did not live near any of the other four.

	drum	flute	gourd	horn	lyre	Ekum	Elfum	Epum	Eskum	Evum
Ekum	–	–	–	–	+	–	–	+	–	–
Elfum	–	+	–	–	–	–	–	–	+	–
Epum	+	–	–	–	–	+	–	–	–	–
Eskum	–	–	–	+	–	–	+	–	–	–
Evum	–	–	+	–	–	–	–	–	–	–

SUMMARY SOLUTION

Ekum	lyre	Epum
Elfum	flute	Eskum
Epum	drum	Ekum
Eskum	horn	Elfum
Evum	gourd	—

S3–4 A SKIRMISH

CONSIDERATIONS

From statements 1 and 4, Som, who used a staff, was the giant. Also from statement 1, Tor was an ogre, and did not use a staff. Therefore, he used a club, since, from statement 3, the sling was used by one of the goblins. From statement 5, Opi was the second ogre. From statement 2, since we know that Tor did not use a staff, that was the weapon wielded by Opi.

Conclusions at this point are:

	giant	goblin	ogre	club	sling	staff
Opi	−	−	+	−	−	+
Rido	−		−			
Som	+	−	−	−	−	+
Sumo	−		−			
Tor	−	−	+	+	−	−
Zeb	−		−			
club	−		+			
sling	−		−			
staff	+	−	+			

The three goblins must have been Rido, Sumo, and Zeb.

From statement 6, since Tor and Zeb used different weapons, Zeb must have used the sling; Rido and Sumo used clubs.

SUMMARY SOLUTION

Opi	ogre	staff
Rido	goblin	club
Som	giant	staff
Sumo	goblin	club
Tor	ogre	club
Zeb	goblin	sling

S3–5 POTLUCK DINNER

From statements 1, 3, and 4, neither Ebum, Epum, Eskum, nor Evum was the first to arrive, so did not bring the soup. Since we know that Ekum was late in arriving, the first to arrive was Elfum, who provided the soup.

From statements 2, 4, and 5, Ebum must have been the last to arrive and brought the fish. Since Epum preceded Evum and Eskum, who was not last, he must have been either second or third to arrive.

From statement 6, Epum was not third, so must have been second. Evum was third and provided mushrooms, and Eskum was fourth to arrive. Therefore, Ekum was fifth to arrive.

The conclusions, so far, are:

	dessert	fish	greens	mushrooms	nuts	soup	1st	2nd	3rd	4th	5th	6th
Ebum	−	+	−	−	−	−	−	−	−	−	−	+
Ekum		−		−		−	−	−	−	−	+	−
Elfum	−	−	−	−	−	+	+	−	−	−	−	−
Epum		−		−		−	−	+	−	−	−	−
Eskum		−		−		−	−	−	−	+	−	−
Evum	−	−	−	+	−	−	−	−	+	−	−	−
1st	−	−	−	−	−	+						
2nd		−		−		−						
3rd	−	−	−	+	−	−						
4th		−		−		−						
5th		−		−		−						
6th	−	+	−	−	−	−						

From statement 7, Epum, who was second to arrive, brought the dessert. From statement 2, Ekum, who did not provide the dessert, provided the nuts. Therefore, the greens were provided by Eskum.

SUMMARY SOLUTION

Ebum	fish	sixth
Ekum	nuts	fifth
Elfum	soup	first
Epum	dessert	second
Eskum	greens	fourth
Evum	mushrooms	third

S3–6 ATHLETIC COMPETITION

CONSIDERATIONS

Consider that there were only three of the six who entered any of the four events and each event was won by a different Minikin.

From statements 2, 3, and 5, Ekum, Evum, and Eskum were the three who entered the distance run. From statements 2, 3, and 7, Ekum, Evum, and Epum were the three who entered the tree climb. From statements 6 and 4, Ebum did not enter the spear throw. Therefore, from statement 6, Ebum won the log lift.

We know that Ekum, Evum, and Epum entered the tree climb. From statement 1, the winner of that event did not enter the distance run. Therefore, since Ekum and Evum entered the distance run, Epum won the tree climb.

So far, the conclusions are:

	Ebum enter	won	Ekum enter	won	Elfum enter	won	Epum enter	won	Eskum enter	won	Evum enter	won
run	−	−	+		−	−	−	−	+		+	
lift	+	+		−		−		−		−		−
throw	−	−										
climb	−	−	+	−	−	−	+	+	−	−	+	−

From statement 5, Elfum was one of the winners. Therefore, Elfum must have won the spear throw. Also from statement 5, Eskum was one of the winners, and must have won the distance run. From statement 4, the winner of the spear throw, Elfum, also entered the log lift. From statement 7, Epum entered the log lift, and Eskum entered the spear throw.

SUMMARY SOLUTION

	entered	won
Ebum	lift	lift
Ekum	run, climb	—
Elfum	throw, lift	throw
Epum	lift, climb	climb
Eskum	run, throw	run
Evum	run, throw, climb	—

S3–7 RIVER TRIP

CONSIDERATIONS

From statement 1, neither Ekum, Elfum, nor Egum was on raft #2; at least one was on raft #1; at least one was on raft

#3. From statements 3, 4, and 5, Ebum and Ekum were on the same raft, but not with Evum; Egum and Eskum were on raft #3, but not with Evum. Therefore, Ebum and Ekum were on raft #1; Evum was on raft #2. From statement 2, Epum and Edum must have been on raft #2 with Evum.

Our conclusions, so far, are:

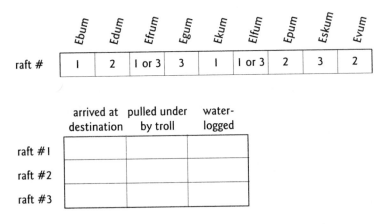

	Ebum	Edum	Efrum	Egum	Ekum	Elfum	Epum	Eskum	Evum
raft #	1	2	1 or 3	3	1	1 or 3	2	3	2

	arrived at destination	pulled under by troll	water-logged
raft #1			
raft #2			
raft #3			

From statements 2 and 3, raft #2 did not become waterlogged, nor was it pulled underwater by a troll. Therefore, raft #2 arrived at the predetermined destination. From statement 4, raft #1 did not become waterlogged. Therefore, it was pulled underwater by a troll, and raft #3 became waterlogged. From statement 6, Efrum was not on the raft that was pulled underwater by a troll. Therefore, he was on raft #3, and Elfum was on raft #1.

SUMMARY SOLUTION

raft #1   Ebum, Ekum, and Elfum   pulled under by a troll
raft #2   Edum, Epum, and Evum   arrived at destination
raft #3   Egum, Efrum, and Eskum   became waterlogged

CONSIDERATIONS

From statement 5, since Elfum placed third in singing and did not place in acorn gathering, he was second in dancing and must have been first in huckleberry eating. From statement 3, since Evum was not first in acorn gathering or dancing, and we know that Elfum was first in huckleberry eating, Evum was first in singing. From statement 2, Evum was third in huckleberry eating.

At this point our conclusions are:

	acorn gathering			dancing			singing			huckleberry eating		
	1st	2nd	3rd	1st	2nd	3rd	1st	2nd	3rd	1st	2nd	3rd
Ekum					−		−		−	−		−
Elfum	−	−	−	−	+	−	−	−	+	+	−	−
Eskum					−		−		−	−		−
Evum	−			−	−		+	−	−	−	−	+

From statement 4, Evum must have been second in acorn gathering, behind Eskum. Ekum's first place was in dancing; his third place must have been in acorn gathering. Eskum's third place must have been in dancing, and, from statement 1, his second place was in huckleberry eating. Ekum's second place was in singing.

SUMMARY SOLUTION

	acorn gathering	dancing	singing	huckleberry eating
Ekum	third	first	second	—
Elfum	—	second	third	first
Eskum	first	third	—	second
Evum	second	—	first	third

S4–1 APOLLO MEETS TWO

CONSIDERATIONS

Assume A is a Nororean as B's statement indicates. If so, from A's statement, B is also a Nororean, since A's statement must be false. However, if so, B cannot be a Nororean, since this would mean his statement was truthful, and Nororeans always speak falsely. Therefore, B, who has spoken falsely, is a Nororean; A, who has spoken falsely, but is not a Nororean, is a Midrorean.

	Sororean	Nororean	Midrorean
A	–	–	+
B	–	+	–

SUMMARY SOLUTION

A. Midrorean
B. Nororean

S4–2 APOLLO MEETS TWO MORE

CONSIDERATIONS

A's second statement must be false. It would be true only for a Nororean, and Nororeans always speak falsely. Therefore, A must be a Midrorean. A's first statement must be true. Therefore, B is either a Sororean or a Nororean.

B's first statement is truthful, since we know A to be a Midrorean. Therefore, B's second statement must also be true (B cannot be a Nororean). B is a Sororean.

	Sororean	Nororean	Midrorean
A	–	–	+
B	+	–	–

SUMMARY SOLUTION

A. Midrorean
B. Sororean

S4–3 DELEGATION FROM ÆTHIOPIA

CONSIDERATIONS

B's first statement contains two parts. If both parts are false, the statement is false; if either part is true the statement is true. Assume the statement is false. This means that B must be a Sororean, but Sororeans only speak truthfully. Therefore, the statement must be true. B cannot be a Nororean, as Nororeans only speak falsely. B must be a Midrorean.

If either part of A's statement is false the statement is false. Since we know B to be a Midrorean, A's statement is false; A is not a Sororean. B's second statement claims that A is a Midrorean. B's first statement, however, is true, so the second statement is false. A is a Nororean.

	Sororean	Nororean	Midrorean
A	–	+	–
B	–	–	+

SUMMARY SOLUTION

A. Nororean
B. Midrorean

S4–4 WHO SPEAKS TRUTHFULLY?

CONSIDERATIONS

Assume that A is the Sororean. If so, then B is the Nororean as A's second statement asserts. If so, B's second statement, that C is the Midrorean, must be false. However, since one of the three is the Midrorean, A cannot be the Sororean.

Assume that B is the Sororean. If so, C is the Midrorean, as B claims. Both of C's statements would be false, however, revealing C to be the Nororean, contradicting B's claim. Therefore, B is not the Sororean. Therefore, C is the

Sororean; A is the Midrorean, as C indicates; and B is the Nororean.

	Sororean	Nororean	Midrorean
A	–	–	+
B	–	+	–
C	+	–	–

SUMMARY SOLUTION

A. Midrorean
B. Nororean
C. Sororean

S4–5 WHO WON THE OLIVE WREATH?

CONSIDERATIONS

Assume that A's first statement is truthful. If so, B's first statement and C's second statement are both false, and A must be the Sororean. However, A's second statement implies that C is the Sororean. Therefore, A is not the Sororean. Either A's second statement is false or his first and third statements are false, or all three statements are false.

B's second statement must be true. If it were false, C would be the Nororean and there could be no Sororean among the three. Therefore, one of B and C is the Sororean, the other the Midrorean, and A is the Nororean. A's statement implying that C is the Sororean is false. C is the Midrorean, and B is the Sororean. As B indicates, A won the race.

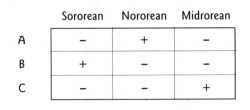

	Sororean	Nororean	Midrorean
A	–	+	–
B	+	–	–
C	–	–	+

SUMMARY SOLUTION

A. Nororean, winner
B. Sororean
C. Midrorean

S4–6 THE CENTAUR PROPHET

CONSIDERATIONS

Assume that C's first statement is false. If so, the Sororean must be either A or B. If A, that means that A's third statement must be true and C is a Nororean, which means that C's second statement must be false, which means that A cannot be the Sororean; so it must be B. This cannot be, however because, if C were the Nororean and B were the Sororean, A must be the Midrorean; but both A's first and second statements would be false and A would be the Nororean.

Therefore, C's first statement must be true. This means that the fourth individual is a Midrorean, as only a Midrorean can claim to be a Nororean. It follows that B's first statement is true, and B is either the Midrorean or the Sororean. C's second statement must be false, otherwise both A and C would be Sororeans. C is the Midrorean; B is the Sororean; and A is the Nororean.

	Sororean	Nororean	Midrorean
A	–	+	–
B	+	–	–
C	–	–	+
fourth	–	–	+

SUMMARY SOLUTION

A. Nororean
B. Sororean
C. Midrorean
fourth   Midrorean

CONSIDERATIONS

The Outlier must make two, but not three, consecutive statements that are both truthful or both false.

Assume that B's first statement is false. If so, D's second statement is also false, as is C's second statement. A's second statement is false, as we know the forepart of the chimaera's body was that of a lion, and the hind part was that of a dragon. Therefore, since one of the four is a Sororean, B's first statement must be truthful, as are C's second statement and D's second statement. Therefore, A must be the Nororean.

B's third statement, which agrees with A's false second statement, is false. Since B's first statement is truthful and third statement is false, B is the Outlier.

Since D was overheard to claim to be a Nororean (B's first statement, which is truthful), D cannot be the Sororean. Therefore, C is the Sororean.

Our conclusions, so far, are:

	Sororean	Nororean	Midrorean	Outlier
A	−	+	−	−
B	−	−	−	+
C	+	−	−	−
D	−	−		−

It follows that D is the Midrorean, whose second statement is true, and first and third statements are false.

SUMMARY SOLUTION

    A. Nororean
    B. Outlier
    C. Sororean
    D. Midrorean

S4–8 WHO IS THE OUTLIER?

CONSIDERATIONS

Assume that A is the Outlier as B's third statement indicates. If so, B is either the Sororean or the Midrorean, and B's first statement must be true. If B is the Sororean, D is the Midrorean, as B's second statement indicates, and C must be the Nororean. However, C's second statement indicates that B is the Sororean. Therefore, since Nororeans cannot speak truthfully, B would not be the Sororean. If B is the Midrorean, C is the Nororean, as indicated by B's first statement, and it follows that D is the Sororean. However, D's second statement contradicts B's third statement. Therefore, A is not the Outlier.

Assume that B is the Outlier. If so, A's third statement, indicating that B is not the Outlier, is false, as is A's first statement. C must be either the Sororean or the Midrorean. However, C's second and third statements would both be false. Therefore, B is not the Outlier.

Assume that D is the Outlier. If so, A must be the Sororean, as B's third statement is false, as is C's third statement. B, whose first statement falsely claims that C is less truthful than B, must be the Nororean, and C must be the Midrorean. However, C's second statement is also false, and C would be the Nororean. Therefore, D is not the Outlier. Therefore, by elimination, C is the Outlier.

Our conclusions at this point are:

	Sororean	Nororean	Midrorean	Outlier
A				–
B				–
C	–	–	–	+
D				–

B must be the Nororean, as A and D have made at least one truthful statement. D is the Sororean, as B's second statement falsely claims that D is the Midrorean. A, whose first and third statements are truthful and second statement is false, is the Midrorean.

SUMMARY SOLUTION

A. Midrorean
B. Nororean
C. Outlier
D. Sororean

S4–9 SOME ARE MORE EQUAL THAN OTHERS

CONSIDERATIONS

Assume that Phaeton's second statement, implying that Epimetheus is not the Nororean, is false. If so, Epimetheus' first statement, Gordius' second statement and Vertumnus' third statement, which are in agreement, are also false. However, since we know that two of the five Hyperboreans are Sororeans, who always speak truthfully, the four statements cannot all be false. Therefore, they must be true. Therefore, since Epimetheus, Gordius, Phaeton, and Vertumnus have at least one true statement each, Iphis must be the Nororean, with all false statements.

Vertumnus' first statement confirms Iphis' first statement, which is false. Since Vertumnus' third statement is true and first statement is false, his standard of veracity is not consistent with any of the three Hyperborean conventional standards. Therefore, Vertumnus is the Outlier.

Iphis' fourth statement falsely indicates that Gordius is not the Midrorean. Therefore, Gordius is the Midrorean, whose second and fourth statements are truthful, and first and third statements are false. Therefore, Epimetheus and Phaeton are the two Sororeans, with all truthful statements.

Our conclusions at this point are:

	Sororean	Nororean	Midrorean	Outlier	job	rank in age
Epimetheus	+	−	−	−		
Gordius	−	−	+	−		
Iphis	−	+	−	−		
Phaeton	+	−	−	−		
Vertumnus	−	−	−	+		

Epimetheus is the blacksmith, as claimed. Gordius' first statement, which is false, indicates that he is not the olive picker. Therefore, Gordius is the olive picker.

Phaeton is a shepherd as claimed. Gordius' third statement, which is false, indicates that Iphis is not the fisherman. Therefore, Iphis is the fisherman. Therefore, Vertumnus is the second shepherd.

Gordius, as claimed in his fourth statement, is the oldest. The fisherman (Iphis) is the youngest, as indicated by Epimetheus. The blacksmith (Epimetheus) is the third oldest, as indicated by Phaeton. Therefore, Phaeton, the older of the two shepherds, as claimed, is the second oldest. Therefore, Vertumnus is the fourth oldest.

SUMMARY SOLUTION

		job	*rank in age*
Epimetheus	Sororean	blacksmith	3rd oldest
Gordius	Midrorean	olive picker	oldest
Iphis	Nororean	fisherman	youngest
Phaeton	Sororean	shepherd	2nd oldest
Vertumnus	Outlier	shepherd	4th oldest

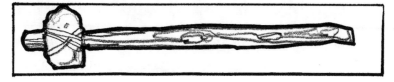

S5–1 RABBITS PLAY HOCKEY

CONSIDERATIONS

From statements 1, 6, and 2, some alligators carry umbrellas in the shower, know that flying fish live in the trees, and prefer caramel candy to chocolate.

From statements 4, 7, and 8, some large reptiles are steeplechasers; they are the ones that prefer caramel candy to chocolate, and they are vegetarians.

From statements 3 and 5, certain days are set aside for alligators to watch rabbits play hockey, but this is limited to those alligators that are steeplechasers.

INFERENCE

Only alligators that are vegetarians are allowed to watch rabbits play hockey.

S5–2 GORILLAS ENJOY BALLET

CONSIDERATIONS

From statements 1, 9, and 7, gorillas enjoy ballet, do not handle hot ice cubes, and travel to town in leaky rowboats.

From statements 5, 8, and 4, gorillas do not have the penultimate word in a verbal discourse, do not play solitaire, and are immune from hay fever.

From statements 6, 3, and 2, Scotch broom gives animals hay fever, it blooms every Thursday all over Mars, and all animals can fly to Mars.

INFERENCE

All animals can fly to Mars, but gorillas are among the few animals that should go there on Thursdays.

S5–3 NO BOOKS IN THE SECOND SOLAR PERIOD OF THE WEEK

CONSIDERATIONS

From statements 1, 5, 6 and 9, curly-maned mountain lions are able to take the fourth solar period of the week off since they earn maximum credits and, therefore, obey the book law.

From statements 7 and 3, it is evident that it always snows in the fourth solar period of each week in the first lunar period of the season.

From statements 8 and 4, it is evident that curly-maned mountain lions go sailing in the first lunar period of the season. However, from statement 2, we know that curly-maned mountain lions never get snowed on while sailing.

INFERENCE

Curly-maned mountain lions go sailing in the first lunar period of the season, but not in the fourth solar period of the week.

S5–4 SENTIENT BEINGS

CONSIDERATIONS

From statements 1, and 6, huckleberry mush is delivered universally and enjoyed by all sentient beings.

From statements 3, 7 and 5, aliens from other galaxies enjoy watching fish ski, are avid chess players, and are numismatists.

From statements 2, 9, 4, and 8, numismatists understand about nutrition, are capable of leaping tall buildings but do not do it often, and like their food chilled.

INFERENCE

Aliens from other galaxies enjoy chilled huckleberry mush.

S5–5 NEIGHBORS MAKE GOOD FENCES

CONSIDERATIONS

From statements 1, 8, 4 and 6, platypuses that are neighbors make good fences and, since they are certified chefs, having attended the Hayberry Island Culinary Institute, they make purple popcorn.

From statements 10, 3, 7 and 9, striped otters have a variety of fishing lures, but those that use woolly worms are true anglers and are the ones to receive invitations to good fences to sit and eat purple popcorn.

From statements 2, 11 and 5, purple popcorn can only be eaten in specially designated places (i.e., per statement 9, sitting on good fences), platypuses do not eat sitting down, and no mammal stands on fences.

INFERENCE

Purple popcorn is made by the platypuses that make good fences, but it is only eaten by striped otters that fish with woolly worms.

S6–1 TWO INHABITANTS

CONSIDERATIONS

It was given that one is an Amtru, and one is a Pemtru.

Assume it is morning. If so, A, who claims that B is the Amtru, must be the Pemtru. However, this would be the truth, which is not possible for a Pemtru in the morning. Therefore, it must be afternoon. A is the Pemtru, and B is the Amtru, as truthfully stated by A.

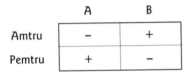

	A	B
Amtru	–	+
Pemtru	+	–

SUMMARY SOLUTION It is afternoon; A is the Pemtru; B is the Amtru.

S6–2 TWO INHABITANTS AGAIN

CONSIDERATIONS

Consider that one is an Amtru, and one is a Pemtru.

Assume A is the Pemtru. If it is morning, a Pemtru would have to speak falsely. If it is afternoon, a Pemtru would have to speak truthfully. Therefore, A is an Amtru, as only an Amtru can claim it is morning. If the statement is true, it is morning. If the statement is false, it is afternoon.

Assume it is afternoon. If so, A's statement is false. However, B, who must be the Pemtru, asserts that A is a Pemtru, which we know is false. Therefore, it is morning. A has spoken truthfully. B, who falsely claims that A is the Pemtru, is a Pemtru.

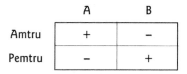

	A	B
Amtru	+	−
Pemtru	−	+

SUMMARY SOLUTION It is morning; A is an Amtru; B is a Pemtru.

S6–3 TWO INHABITANTS ONCE AGAIN

CONSIDERATIONS

Assume it is afternoon. If so, A's statement must be false. A must be an Amtru and B must be a Pemtru. If it is afternoon, this is the only possibility, as a Pemtru's statement must be true and an Amtru's statement must be false. However, B's statement that A is a Pemtru must be false—not possible for a Pemtru in the afternoon.

Therefore, it is morning. Either A and B are both Amtrus, as truthfully stated by A; or else A is a Pemtru, who has made a false statement, and B could be either an Amtru or a Pemtru. From B's statement, we can conclude that it is true: A is a Pemtru and B is an Amtru.

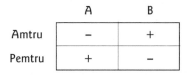

	A	B
Amtru	–	+
Pemtru	+	–

SUMMARY SOLUTION

It is morning; A is a Pemtru, and B is an Amtru.

S6–4 THREE INHABITANTS

CONSIDERATIONS

Consider that two are Amtrus and one is a Pemtru.

Assume it is afternoon. If so, A's statement must be false, as it would be true only if A were a Pemtru, and this would mean two Pemtrus. Therefore, if it is afternoon, A and B are Amtrus, and C is the Pemtru. However, if it is afternoon, C, whose statement must be true, claims that A is the Pemtru., which would be false, a contradiction.

Therefore, it must be morning. If A is an Amtru, his statement is true, and B is the Pemtru. If so, from B's false statement, C is also a Pemtru.

However, since we know there are two Amtrus, B and C, who have both spoken truthfully, are Amtrus. A, who has falsely claimed that B is the Pemtru, is the Pemtru.

	A	B	C
Amtru	–	+	+
Pemtru	+	–	–

SUMMARY SOLUTION

It is morning; A is the Pemtru, and B and C are Amtrus.

S6–5 THREE INHABITANTS AGAIN

CONSIDERATIONS

Consider that there are two Pemtrus and one Amtru.

Assume it is morning. If so, if C is the Amtru, his statement is true and A is a Pemtru. If so, A's statement is false and B is a Pemtru. If so, B's statement is false and C is a Pemtru, which is a contradiction.

Therefore, if it is morning, C is a Pemtru. If so, C's statement is false, and A is the Amtru. If so, A's statement is true, and B is an Amtru. If so, B's statement is true, and C is an Amtru, which is a contradiction (as well as providing for more than one Amtru).

Therefore, it is afternoon. Assume C is the Amtru. If so, C's statement is false, and A is also an Amtru. However, since we know there is only one Amtru, C is a Pemtru. C's statement is true; A is a Pemtru. A's statement is also true; B is the Amtru.

	A	B	C
Amtru	−	+	−
Pemtru	+	−	+

SUMMARY SOLUTION
It is afternoon; A and C are Pemtrus; B is an Amtru.

S6–6 MORNING AND AFTERNOON

CONSIDERATIONS
A must be an Amtru. If he were a Pemtru, E's statement would not be possible. It is made in the afternoon and claims a different group than A's. If E were a Pemtru, his statement would be true. If E were an Amtru, his statement would be false.

B, who disputes A's statement, is a Pemtru, as is C, who agrees with B. D is a Pemtru, as he truthfully states that B is a Pemtru. F has told an afternoon lie, since he states that A and D are from the same group. Therefore F is an Amtru.

E could be either an Amtru, who has told an afternoon lie, or a Pemtru, whose statement is truthful.

	A	B	C	D	E	F
Amtru	+	−	−	−	?	+
Pemtru	−	+	+	+	?	−

SUMMARY SOLUTION

A and F are Amtrus; B, C, and D are Pemtrus. E could be either an Amtru or a Pemtru.

S6–7 FOUR INHABITANTS

CONSIDERATIONS

Consider that B and C are not both Amtrus.
    From C's statement, we can conclude the following:

1. C could be a Pemtru in the afternoon, in which case C has spoken truthfully, and A is a Pemtru.
2. C could be a Pemtru in the morning, in which case C has spoken falsely and A is an Amtru.
3. C could be an Amtru in the afternoon, in which case C has spoken falsely and A is either an Amtru or a Pemtru.

Assume it is afternoon. If so, and if C is a Pemtru, C has spoken the truth and A is a Pemtru. If so, D's statement is false; A would not claim that he and C do not belong to the same group. D would be an Amtru. If so, B's statement is false, since as an Amtru, D would falsely state that he and A belong to the same group; B would be an Amtru. If so, however, A's statement falsely asserts that B would claim to belong to the same group as D. Therefore, if it is afternoon, C is not a Pemtru.

Assume that it is afternoon and C is an Amtru. Also assume that A is an Amtru. If so, D's statement is true: A would falsely indicate that he and C belong to different groups. D would be a Pemtru. If so, B's statement is true: D would truthfully indicate that he and A belong to different groups. B would be a Pemtru. A's statement, however, would be true, which is impossible for an Amtru in the afternoon. Therefore, if it is afternoon and C is an Amtru; A is not an Amtru.

Assume that it is afternoon, C is an Amtru, and A is a Pemtru. If so, D's statement is true; D would be a Pemtru. If so, B's statement would be false; B would be an Amtru. However, since it was given that B and C were not both Amtrus, it must be morning.

Therefore, C is a Pemtru and A is an Amtru. D has truthfully stated that A would truthfully assert that he and C belong to different groups; D is an Amtru. B, who falsely states that D would claim a different group than A, is a Pemtru.

	A	B	C	D
Amtru	+	−	−	+
Pemtru	−	+	+	−

SUMMARY SOLUTION
It is morning; A and D are Amtrus; B and C are Pemtrus.

About the Author

NORMAN D. WILLIS is a retired international management consultant. He lives with his wife on an island in the Puget Sound. This is Mr. Willis' second book. His first book, *Amazing Logic Puzzles*, was published by Sterling Publishing Co., Inc., in 1994.

Index

Adventures of Captain Jean Lafoot, the Pirate, The, 13–19, 49–51, 63–71

Another Dragon, 9, 48, **59**

Apollo Meets Two, 29, 56, **80**

Apollo Meets Two More, 29, 56, **80**

Athletic Competion, 25–26, 54–55, **76–77**

Autumn Festival and Games, 27, 55, **79**

Buccaneer Quartet, 15, 50, **65**

Centaur Prophet, The, 32–33, 56, **83**

Chase on the Open Sea, A, 14, 49–50, **64**

Chimaera in the Land, A, 34–35, 57, **84**

Delegation from Æthiopia, 30, 56, **81**

Dragons of Lidd, The, 8–12, 48, **59**

Four Dragons, 12, 49, **62–63**

Four Inhabitants, 47, 58, **94–95**

Gorillas Enjoy Ballet, 39–40, (57), **88**

Hints, 48–58

Homes of the Minikins, 21–22, 52, **72**

Hyperborea, 28–37, 56–57, **80–87**

Island Fish, The, 16–17, 50, **66–67**

Land of Liars, The, 43–47, 57–58, **90–95**

Minikins, The, 20–27, 52–55, **71–79**

Morning and Afternoon, 46–47, 58, **93–94**

Musicians, 23, 53, **73**

Musket Competition, The, 17, 51, **67–68**

Narrow Escapes, 21, 52, **71–72**

Neighbors Make Good Fences, 42, (57), **90**

No Books in the Second Solar Period of the Week, 40, (57), **89**

Nonsense, 38–42, 57, **88–90**

One Dragon, 9, 48, **59**

One Overslept, 14, 49, **63–64**

Potluck Dinner, 25, 54, **75–76**

Puzzles, 8–47

Rabbits Play Hockey, 39, (57), **88**

River Trip, 26–27, 55, **77–78**

Sea Serpent, A, 15–16, 50, **66**

Sea Serpent Returns, The, 19, 51, **69–71**

Sentient Beings, 41, (57), **89**

Skirmish, A, 24, 53, **74**

Solutions, 59–95

Some Are More Equal Than Others, 36–37, 57, **86–87**

Three and One, 11, 49, **62**

Three Dragons, 10, 49, **60–61**

Three Inhabitants, 45, 58, **92**

Three Inhabitants Again, 46, 58, **92–93**

Two Colors, 10, 48, **60**

Two Inhabitants, 44, 57, **90**

Two Inhabitants Again, 44, 57, **91**

Two Inhabitants Once Again, 45, 58, **91–92**

Two Types, 9, 48, **59**

Who Is the Outlier?, 35–36, 57, **85–86**

Who Speaks the Truth?, 11, 49, **61**

Who Speaks Truthfully?, 31, 56, **81–82**

Who Won the Olive Wreath?, 32, 56, **82–83**

Whose Hair Turned White?, 18–19, 51, **68–69**

Page key: Puzzle, *hints*, **solution.**